'Lunatic'

THE BEST OF
MATT
2020

MATTHEW PRITCHETT
studied at St Martin's School of Art in
London and first saw himself published
in the *New Statesman* during one of its rare
lapses from high seriousness. He has been
the *Daily Telegraph*'s front-page pocket
cartoonist since 1988. In 1995, 1996, 1999,
2005, 2009 and 2013 he was the winner of
the Cartoon Arts Trust Award and in 1991,
2004 and 2006 he was 'What the Papers
Say' Cartoonist of the Year. In 1996, 1998,
2000, 2008, 2009, 2018 and 2019 he was
the *UK Press* Cartoonist of the Year and in
2015 he was awarded the Journalists'
Charity Award. In 2002 he received an MBE.

Own your favourite Matt cartoons.
Browse the full range of Matt
cartoons and buy online at
www.telegraph.co.uk/mattprints
or call 0191 6030178.

'Sometimes I wish we could go back to living in precedented times'

The Daily Telegraph

THE BEST OF
MATT
2020

SEVEN DIALS

First published in Great Britain in 2020 by Seven Dials
A division of the Orion Publishing Group Ltd
Carmelite House
50 Victoria Embankment
London
EC4Y 0DZ

A Hachette UK Company

10 9 8 7 6 5 4 3 2 1

A CIP catalogue record for this book is available from the British Library.

ISBN: 978 1 4091 9148 3

Printed in Italy by Elcograf S.p.A

The Orion Publishing Group's policy is to use papers that are natural,
renewable and recyclable products and made from wood grown in
sustainable forests. The logging and manufacturing processes are
expected to conform to the environmental regulations of the country of
origin.

www.orionbooks.co.uk

'I told the HS2 builders
I had coronavirus'

THE BEST OF
MATT
2020

'I'm sorry, but this is the only way to stop the spread of the coronavirus'

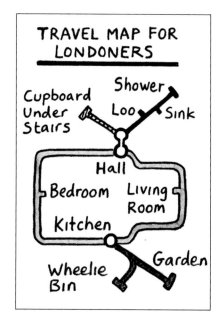

Coronavirus

'And this property comes with a granny flat'

'Loo roll for sale, £350,000.
Comes with two
bedroom flat'

'There'll be loo rolls over
The white cliffs of Dover
Tomorrow, just you wait
and see'

Coronavirus

'Not murder, Sarge.
We're searching for a
serial sunbather'

FOR MARK & ANNE
WHO WERE FINED FOR
SITTING HERE DURING
LOCKDOWN. APRIL 2020

'Have you noticed you see far fewer humans around these days?'

'Darling, I can explain!
I went for a second run, but it
will never happen again'

'Easter egg o' clock is getting
earlier every day'

SIGHTSEEING DISCOURAGED

BEAUTY SPOT

'From up here you can see
four contradictory rules
on exercising outdoors'

'I volunteered to do my bit during the pandemic. They asked me to be PM or Health Secretary'

'To be on the safe side I've put our Duchy Original biscuits in isolation'

PM and Royals succumb

'Stop making ventilators!
The country is crying out
for more jigsaw puzzles'

Coronavirus

'Good news. We could be
a zero carbon business
by next week'

LONDON 1666

'Is this part of the roadmap
out of the Great Plague?'

Coronavirus

'My husband's cooking, so I'm going out to catch coronavirus – apparently you lose all sense of taste and smell'

'If you want peace and quiet this is perfect – it's next to a huge pub and opposite an airport'

Coronavirus

'If you show the early signs of becoming an armchair expert, you must self isolate till 2021'

'Come and stand on the doorstep. We're all going to wag our finger at Professor Neil Ferguson'

Government scientist resigns after breaking lockdown

'If every minister shares the blame for the testing fiasco we might develop a herd immunity'

CORONAVIRUS TEST BREAKTHROUGH

'I have it, I don't have it...'

'We're in danger of missing our target, so we need to test you for coronavirus 32,000 times'

Government close to missing testing target

'I've tested positive for coronavirus. Whomsoever this glass slipper fits should self isolate'

'We catch them humanely, ring them, and release them back into the wild'

'I don't have a smartphone, so I can't download the tracking app'

'I know it's the Cheltenham Festival. I'm working from home'

Cheltenham goes ahead

'It would be a wonderful bank holiday treat if we could all go back to work for one day'

Home schooling stress

'My golf ball remained socially distanced from the flag and hole at all times'

Coronavirus

'Even if we survive the first
wave of tax increases,
there could be a second,
more aggressive spike'

'I hope tax increases can't be passed from humans to bats'

'If you wear it like this you can't see any economic forecasts'

Coronavirus

'Face masks have sold out.
Thank goodness we bought
all that loo roll'

'This is a busy railway,
you fool! We should both
be wearing face masks'

'Well, you're the best
ventriloquist act
I've ever seen'

'We've offered to switch to
making NHS face masks.
They'll cost £500,000 each
and be ready by 2035'

Coronavirus

'I have to wear this when I go out. My wife cut my hair and I look ridiculous'

'You've been asleep for 100 years. We can now buy loo roll and flour, but the hairdressers are still closed'

'Boris was on TV.
I think Dilyn has been
cutting his hair'

'Everyone is supposed to
stay where they are.
Was your journey
really essential?'

Boris and Carrie's new baby

Coronavirus

Dominic Cummings' travels

'Sorry we don't have a
garden. More tea, mum?'

Indoor visits still not allowed

Coronavirus

Coronavirus

'I hope they don't get out of the car; they carry so much disease'

Zoos open

'He'll have grown into it by the time he goes back'

'I've met the man of my dreams. He understands algebra and he can homeschool the children'

'I'm drinking to forget school'

'We're visiting our villa in Tuscany. The only way round quarantine rules is to become an HGV driver'

'I wish the Wimbledon tennis was going ahead. We need the rain'

Controversial quarantine rules

'It's nothing personal, but we must observe social distancing in the workplace'

'The only way we can see our parents is if we start a construction business and hire them to work for us'

Coronavirus

Back to work – at a distance

'You'll have to spend
14 days in quarantine.
It will also give us time
to find your luggage'

'Welcome to the UK.
Here's a list of things to
do and see in your room
for the next 14 days'

Schools begin to open – with social distancing

'I've seen the home schooling you did and I've decided to give your parents intensive one-to-one tutoring'

'Our child's school is being divided into bubbles. We're moving into the catchment area of a better bubble'

Coronavirus

Dear friend/family member, I regret to inform you that you have failed to win a place in our household's new expanded bubble.

CUSTOMER REGISTER

'If Mickey Mouse catches coronavirus we'll have to tell Lord Lucan, Adolf Hitler, Marilyn Monroe...'

'My customers will find it impossible to fight in the car park if they have to stay 2m apart'

'My hairdresser had been in the pub for hours'

'If everyone carries a ball
of string with them we'll
know where they've been'

'Please take my daughter's
hand in marriage. With
all the restrictions on
weddings it will hardly
cost me anything'

'Mr Sunak, we've identified some unusual activity. Please check and confirm the following payments: green jobs £3bn, arts £1.5bn, small firms £15bn, furlough £88bn...'

'A sticky toffee pudding? I think you've helped the economy enough today'

Rishi Sunak's paying

'Eye of newt, spleen of rat and leg of toad. Look, I'm just following the science'

'It's ridiculous that cricket isn't allowed. Nobody in our team has ever caught anything'

'Breakfast on the terrace, wine with lunch and a siesta in the afternoon. It will be just like working from home'

'Hi ho, hi ho, it's off to work we go ... oh no, oh no, we'd better stay at home'

Brexit

Border questions continue

'Rory McIlroy's approach shot landed in the middle of the Irish backstop'

Immigration discussions ongoing

'It's tricky. Free movement for people is ending, but we want to hang on to as many fish as possible'

Brexit

'We can't afford Brexit bongs.
At 11pm on January 31, shake
this tambourine as hard
as you can'

'I'm going to Parliament
Square and I'm taking
my own bongs'

'I thought the 30mph limit was one of those meddling EU laws we'd left behind'

'The Government is now in charge. If a train arrives on time, Big Ben will bong and a special 50p coin will be issued'

PM Boris

'Proroguing Parliament cut short John Bercow's leaving speech by five weeks'

'It hasn't improved the toxic mood in here, but we've paid off the national debt'

'I bought this stamp after
Parliament was prorogued.
Does the Queen look
fed up to you?'

'Somebody has made a
horrible mess and I'm not
clearing it up'

Prorogue ruled illegal

PM Boris

'Another Queen's speech?
Her Majesty has had more
call-outs than a
Whirlpool engineer'

'I remember when a pint
cost a quid, a haircut was
a fiver and you could get
ten DUP votes for £1billion'

Boris loses his majority

'I've just heard all the news from the UK. Don't overdo your efforts to get us back'

Thomas Cook goes bust

'We are calling for an election, but at a frequency only dogs can hear'

Labour reluctant

General Election

'Forget all the pre-election slip ups. Right now is when the proper, official gaffes begin'

'It's my new Lib Dem jumper'

Lib Dem plan to revoke Article 50

'Can I count on you
not to vote for me?'

'After a series of deals and
pacts every candidate
agreed not to stand'

Tactical voting

Labour's confusion

'Spoiler alert. They don't win in the end'

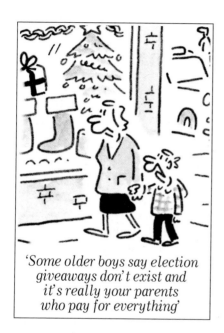

'Some older boys say election giveaways don't exist and it's really your parents who pay for everything'

'And we'll also nationalise Rod Stewart's train set'

Labour's promises

'IT'S TIME FOR
ONE FINAL PUSH'

THE THREE WISE
OPINION POLLSTERS

'I've told every candidate
that I'm voting for them.
This election is all about
honesty and trust'

'Before we come together to
heal our divided country,
let us take a moment to gloat'

Tory victory

General Election

Red Wall falls

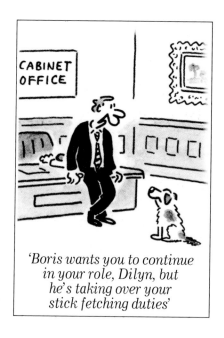

'Boris wants you to continue
in your role, Dilyn, but
he's taking over your
stick fetching duties'

'This is my favourite time
of the year. The season of
blame and recrimination'

The fall-out

'Our aim is to produce totally clean, renewable, zero carbon power cuts'

'That's one of the trees I planted to offset this flight'

'It's all about connectivity. I can attend a climate conference in Exeter and 90 minutes later be at another one in Newcastle'

Flybe in trouble

'I'm just going to plug in our new electric car'

Floods

'We're harnessing the boiling
rage of motorists to power
vehicles of the future'

'I now regret converting
the car to run on coal'

'I'm afraid you've failed your driving test for "deliberately driving a car"'

'I'm worried about the coronavirus. I'm only here to avoid human contact'

Royal Troubles

'We're negotiating a post Brexit trade deal with Canada. We send them our royals and they sell us maple syrup'

'In a joint statement, senior members of the Royal family said they were stepping back from Dry January'

Meghan and Harry leave

Prince Andrew interview

Royal Troubles

Prince withdraws from
Royal duties

'We'll show you a number of
tea towels to see if you can
pick out Prince Andrew'

US lawyers request interview

'Wow, tough crowd'

And finally...

'I've built this painstakingly
accurate scale model
of the HS2 railway line'

'And this is the £10m,
180mph, replacement bus
service for HS2'

'I say we blame the BBC'

'We're having a collection for Lord Hall. It's a fiver for men and a tenner for women'

BBC under attack

And finally...

'This is secret agent Tian Tian calling base. UK to make Huawei announcement soon'

'The President's thought of a new way to protect himself from Covid-19. Go and get a dozen leeches'

'If the Americans won't
agree to buy you, we'll have
to break you up for parts'

'I understand you swam
the Channel four times.
We may need you to bring
vital medicines into the UK'

And finally...

And finally...

'Does Johnny want to come out and head a football?'

Safety concerns

THREE WISE MEN

M23

'I've discovered why we can't
see the Virtual Chelsea
Flower Show. Slugs have
eaten our WiFi router'

And finally...

'My performance in the
Nativity play has been
condemned by the leaders
of all major faiths'

'Dry January is a disaster.
The only people in here
are butchers drinking to
forget Veganuary'

'Captain Tom Moore is walking round his garden again. This time it's to raise money for his TV licence'

'Meet the new team mascot'

Leicester lockdown

And finally...

'It was a waste of time. Apparently there aren't any statues of Michel Barnier'

'Can't anyone here tie a simple knot?'

Statues must fall